MATHS 1

Tens and units, fractions, multiplication tables

Sandra Soper

A Piccolo Original
Piccolo Books

Notes for Parents

The aim of this book is to encourage your child to do maths at home. A great deal will be picked up from your attitude to the work, so when you have time, talk with your child about each activity before you start. Children learn a lot from such conversation and because of it, many mistakes and misunderstandings can be avoided. When a mistake does happen, use it as a learning point rather than a reason for criticism. If you are over-critical, you could put the child off the work altogether. Praise when you can but when there is obviously a lack of effort, say so. Children respect honesty.

In this series we encourage the learning of multiplication tables by heart. It is very useful for the child to have a sound working knowledge of these tables and learning by heart is one way towards this understanding.

Complete the 4+5 pattern up to 100. See how quickly you can fill in the answers to the sums.

+5									
1	2	3	④	5	6	7	8	⑨	10
11	12	13	⑭	15	16	17	18	⑲	20
21	22	23	㉔	25	26	27	28	㉙	30
31	32	33	34	35	36	37	38	39	40
41	42	43	44	45	46	47	48	49	50
51	52	53	54	55	56	57	58	59	60
61	62	63	64	65	66	67	68	69	70
71	72	73	74	75	76	77	78	79	80
81	82	83	84	85	86	87	88	89	90
91	92	93	94	95	96	97	98	99	100

4+5= ☐

14+5= ☐

24+5= ☐

34+5= ☐

44+5= ☐

54+5= ☐

64+5= ☐

74+5= ☐

84+5= ☐

94+5= ☐

Martin did nineteen sums. Fourteen were right and five were wrong. Pick out the sum in this story from the sums above.

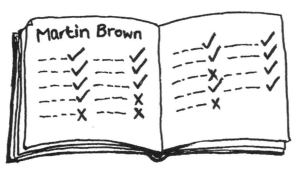

Make up a story of your own to show a different sum from above.

_____

_____

Colour and count the posts in the fence. How many? ☐

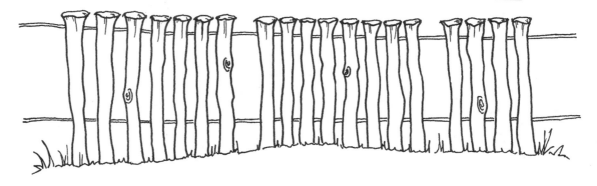

When this fence was new there were 24 posts altogether. How many posts are missing now?

_____

Read the sum about the fence, then write it out in figures underneath.

Twenty-four minus five leaves nineteen

$$\begin{array}{r} 24 \\ -\ 5 \\ \hline 19 \end{array}$$

_____

Use the number lines to help you to take away from 24. Make a number strip like this, so for 24-3 you can see that 21 is left, therefore 24-3=21.

| 1 | 2 | 3 | 4 | 5 | 6 | 7 | 8 | 9 | 10 | 11 | 12 | 13 | 14 | 15 | 16 | 17 | 18 | 19 | 20 | 21 | 22 | 23 | 24 |

| 1 | 2 | 3 | 4 | 5 | 6 | 7 | 8 | 9 | 10 | 11 | 12 | 13 | 14 | 15 | 16 | 17 | 18 | 19 | 20 | 21 | 22 | 23 | 24 |

24-3=   24-24=   24-10=

24-4=   24-20=   24-12=

24-5=   24-21=   24-14=

4

Read the questions aloud before you answer them. Write a word as well as an number for your answer.

What is the total number
of pencils in a box in which
there are four green, six black
and five orange pencils?

_____

Twelve goldfish were taken
from a fish tank to be sold
at the fair. This left eighteen
fish in the tank. How many fish
were there to start with?

_____

Fourteen children from a class of
twenty eight children
went out of the classroom
to see the school nurse.
How many children were left
in the classroom?

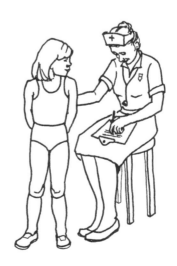

_____

Complete the number chain, then read it aloud. Colour all the multiples of 10.

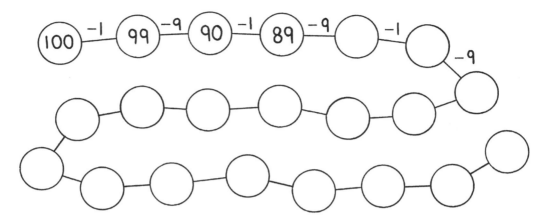

Each child's score is the total of the 2 numbers shown.

Neil   Sue   Amy

Which child shows the highest score? _____

By how much is Neil's score more than Sue's? _____

Whose score is nearest to Amy's? _____

Which score is nearest to 50? _____

Which child shows the lowest score? _____

6

The even numbers are on stripy steps. Go over these numbers, then count them aloud to twenty. Colour the steps under the odd numbers.

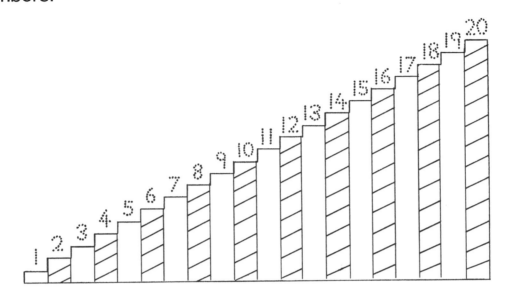

Score out the price on the ticket and write down half this price beside it, then colour the things in the sale.

Write the missing numbers, then read the table aloud.

2 × 1 =
  × 2 = 4
2 × 3 =
2 × 4 =
  × 5 =
2 ×   = 12
2 × 7 =
2 × 8 =
2 ×   = 18
2 × 1 =

Colour every second bead.

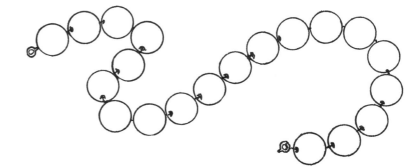

Read the cost of each item aloud.

lollipop   22p   drink   cake

What would be the cost of

2 bars of chocolate? ☐   2 cakes? ☐

2 cans of drink? ☐   2 lollipops? ☐

2 cakes and 2 drinks ☐   2 cakes and 2 lollipops? ☐

Can you divide the marbles equally between Mark and Neil?

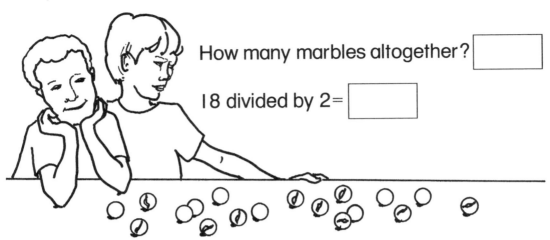

How many marbles altogether? [ ]

18 divided by 2= [ ]

How many marbles will each boy have? Write your answer in a sentence.

_____

How many groups of nine are in eighteen? [ ]

The arrow means <u>divided by 2</u> Can you write in the answers?

| 2 | ⟶ | 1 | | 20 | ⟶ | [ ] |

| 4 | ⟶ | [ ] | | 12 | ⟶ | [ ] |

| 6 | ⟶ | [ ] | | 14 | ⟶ | [ ] |

| 8 | ⟶ | [ ] | | 16 | ⟶ | [ ] |

| 10 | ⟶ | [ ] | | 18 | ⟶ | [ ] |

Use the number line to help you to answer the questions.

```
 1  2  3  4  5  6  7  8  9  10  11  12  13  14  15  16  17  18
```

How many twos in 2? [ ]   How many twos in 8? [ ]

How many twos in 4? [ ]   How many twos in 10? [ ]

How many twos in 6? [ ]   How many twos in 12? [ ]

Colour every second square to make the pattern of the two times table. Use the square to help you to do the sums.

less 2 →
98 →
88 →
78 →
68 →
58 →
48 →
38 →
28 →

1	2	3	4	5	6	7	8	9	10
11	12	13	14	15	16	17	18	19	20
21	22	23	24	25	26	27	28	29	30
31	32	33	34	35	36	37	38	39	40
41	42	43	44	45	46	47	48	49	50
51	52	53	54	55	56	57	58	59	60
61	62	63	64	65	66	67	68	69	70
71	72	73	74	75	76	77	78	79	80
81	82	83	84	85	86	87	88	89	90
91	92	93	94	95	96	97	98	99	100

2 more →
4 →
14 →
24 →
34 →
44 →
54 →
64 →
74 →

Read the questions through before you answer them. Write your answers in a sentence.

Five children each bought two rubbers. How many rubbers is this altogether?

_____

Simon had £3 in his money box. Lisa had two times as much as this. How much money did Lisa have?

_____

David divided 14 beads equally between his 2 sisters. How many beads did each girl have?

_____

Mark the new price on each label.

ALL PRICES <u>DOWN</u> BY 20p

Take twenty from each number. The 100 square on p10 will help.

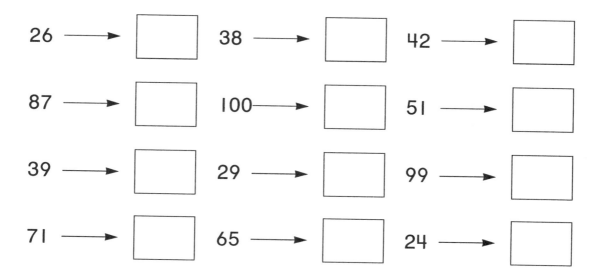

26 ⟶ ☐   38 ⟶ ☐   42 ⟶ ☐

87 ⟶ ☐   100 ⟶ ☐   51 ⟶ ☐

39 ⟶ ☐   29 ⟶ ☐   99 ⟶ ☐

71 ⟶ ☐   65 ⟶ ☐   24 ⟶ ☐

Write words for the answers, then write out the sum in figures.

Eighteen take away seven is | eleven | → | $18 - 7 = 11$

Twenty minus four is | | → | |

Thirty minus twenty is | | → | |

Ninety minus ten is | | → | |

Forty-five less five is | | → | |

Find the difference. Write the word 'difference' after your answers.

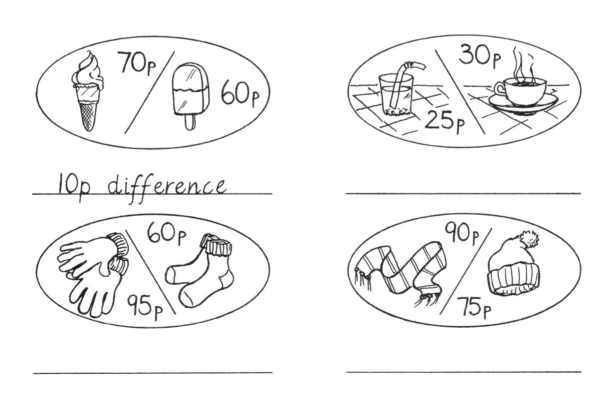

10p difference

_____

_____   _____

There are 100 centimetres in 1 metre. Take these lengths from 1 metre like this:

1m − 20cms (100−20) = | 80 cms |

1m − 50cms (   ) =

1m − 10cms (   ) =

1m − 40cms (   ) =

1m − 60cms (   ) =

1m − 80cms (   ) =

1m − 30cms (   ) =

```
|  |  |  |  |  |  |  |  |  |  |
0  10 20 30 40 50 60 70 80 90 100
```

Use a ruler marked in centimetres to measure these lines.

| 7cms |

Can you do these sums and then read them forwards and backwards?

Count each row of marbles, then put the total in the triangle. Now colour 3 marbles, then write the sum.

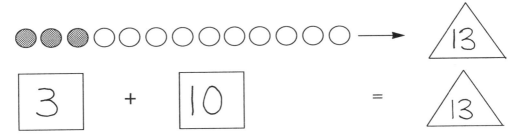

Read the sum forwards and backwards like this,
three and ten equal thirteen, thirteen equals ten and three

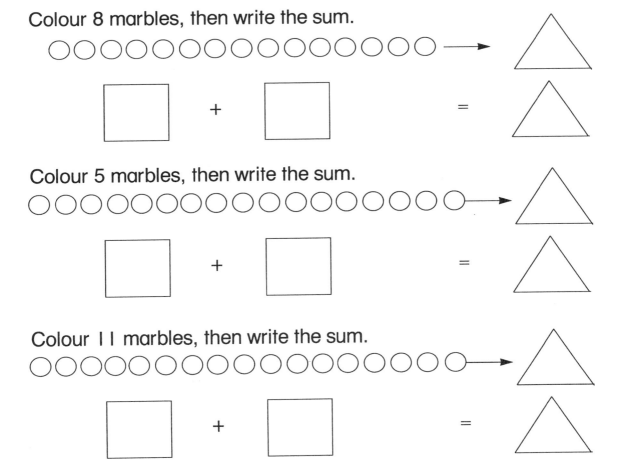

Colour 8 marbles, then write the sum.

Colour 5 marbles, then write the sum.

Colour 11 marbles, then write the sum.

Can you make the scales balance?

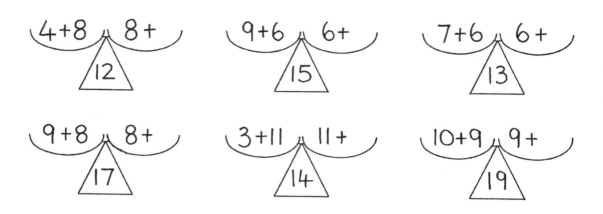

$4+8$ ⚖ $8+$
12

$9+6$ ⚖ $6+$
15

$7+6$ ⚖ $6+$
13

$9+8$ ⚖ $8+$
17

$3+11$ ⚖ $11+$
14

$10+9$ ⚖ $9+$
19

Read the sums along and down. Complete all the boxes.

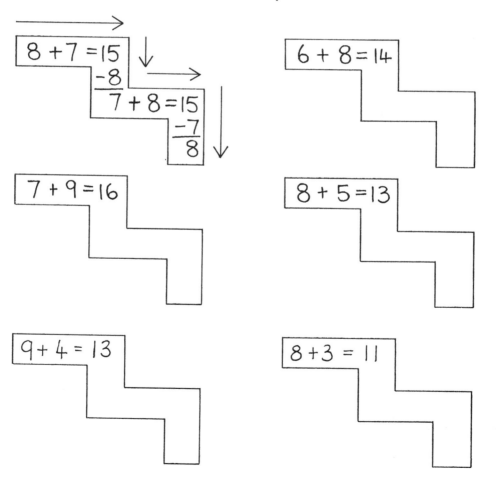

$8+7=15$
-8
$7+8=15$
-7
8

$6+8=14$

$7+9=16$

$8+5=13$

$9+4=13$

$8+3=11$

Write the answers in the boxes.

How many triangles? ☐

How many sides? ☐

How many triangles? ☐

How many sides? ☐

How many triangles? ☐

How many sides? ☐

How many triangles? ☐

How many sides? ☐

Colour every third box to give the pattern of the three times table.
Read the coloured numbers aloud. Finish the sums.

1	2	3	4	5	6	7	8	9	10
11	12	13	14	15	16	17	18	19	20
21	22	23	24	25	26	27	28	29	30
31	32	33	34	35	36	37	38	39	40
41	42	43	44	45	46	47	48	49	50
51	52	53	54	55	56	57	58	59	60
61	62	63	64	65	66	67	68	69	70
71	72	73	74	75	76	77	78	79	80
81	82	83	84	85	86	87	88	89	90
91	92	93	94	95	96	97	98	99	100

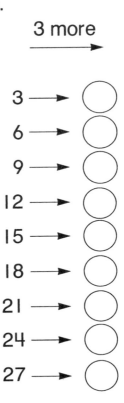

3 more

3 ⟶ ◯
6 ⟶ ◯
9 ⟶ ◯
12 ⟶ ◯
15 ⟶ ◯
18 ⟶ ◯
21 ⟶ ◯
24 ⟶ ◯
27 ⟶ ◯

Complete the three times table then read it aloud.

Colour every third triangle and write its number beside it.

3 X 1 =
3 X 2 =
3 X 3 =
3 X 4 =
3 X 5 =
3 X 6 =
3 X 7 =
3 X 8 =
3 X 9 =
3 X 10 =

Play the spiral game. Choose a spiral. Write numbers 1-30 on scraps of paper and put them in an old margarine tub with a lid. Shake the box, remove the lid, then pick a number. If the number you pick is in the three times table, fill it in the spiral. First to complete the spiral wins. If you are unsure of the table you can check the answers from the table above.

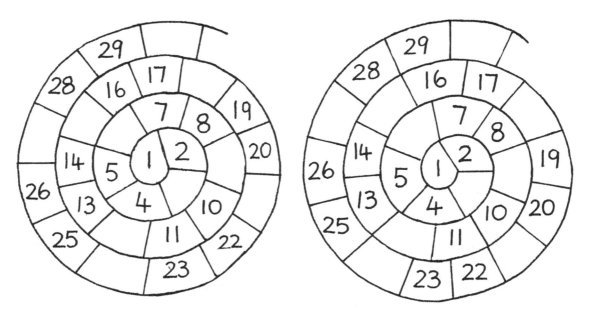

Write words in the answer boxes.

Three times what makes nine?

Three times six equals?

Thirty divided by three is?

How many threes in thirty?

Three times eight is what?

How many threes in twelve?

Each girl is three times as old as her brother. Can you write the age of each girl, then colour the children?

James is 3 years old.

_____

Dan   Joy

James

Sally

Dan is 5 years old. His sister is

_____

Rajiv

Sameena

Rajiv is 4 years old.

_____

Read the question aloud before you write your answers. Write a word as well as a number in each answer. Colour the pictures.

When they came out of the fruit shop, Angela gave three plums to each of her 4 friends. How many plums is this altogether?

_____

John has invited 6 people to his party. He wants to give them each three balloons.
How many balloons must he buy?

_____

How many 3p lollipops could you buy for 30p?

_____

Read the first line aloud, then complete the lines.

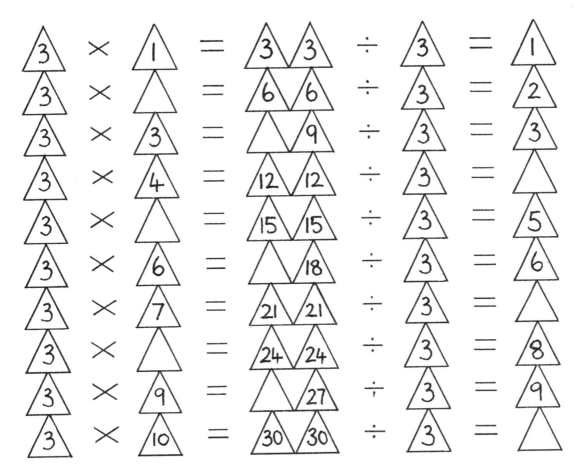

3	×	1	=	3	3	÷	3	=	1
3	×		=	6	6	÷	3	=	2
3	×	3	=		9	÷	3	=	3
3	×	4	=	12	12	÷	3	=	
3	×		=	15	15	÷	3	=	5
3	×	6	=		18	÷	3	=	6
3	×	7	=	21	21	÷	3	=	
3	×		=	24	24	÷	3	=	8
3	×	9	=		27	÷	3	=	9
3	×	10	=	30	30	÷	3	=	

Colour the numbers which can be divided exactly by three.

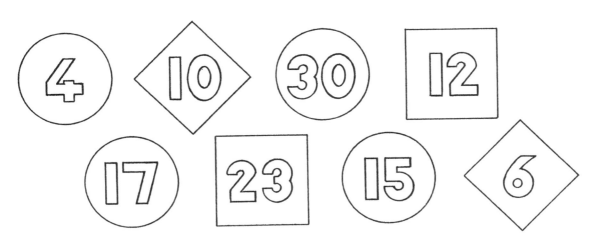

4   10   30   12

17   23   15   6

How many tens in these numbers?

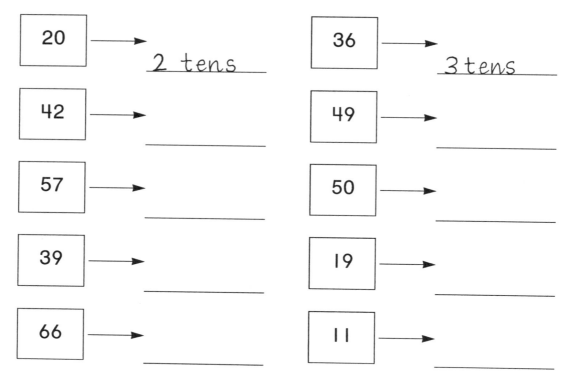

20 →	2 tens	36 →	3 tens
42 →	___	49 →	___
57 →	___	50 →	___
39 →	___	19 →	___
66 →	___	11 →	___

How many units in these numbers?

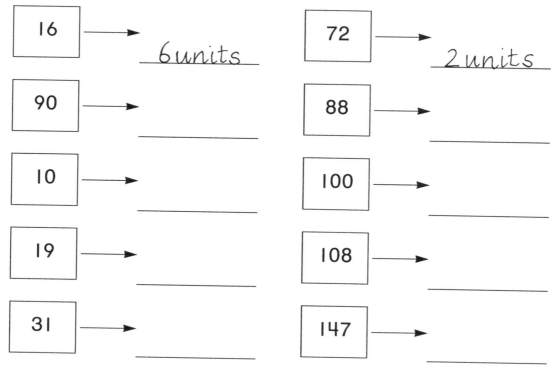

16 →	6 units	72 →	2 units
90 →	___	88 →	___
10 →	___	100 →	___
19 →	___	108 →	___
31 →	___	147 →	___

Write the numbers, then read them aloud like this: 3 tens and 2 units make thirty two.

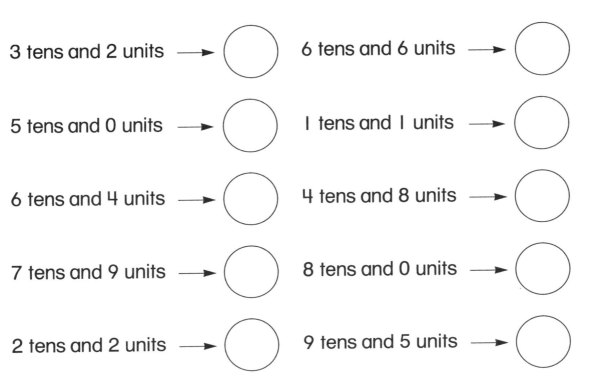

3 tens and 2 units ⟶ ◯   6 tens and 6 units ⟶ ◯

5 tens and 0 units ⟶ ◯   1 tens and 1 units ⟶ ◯

6 tens and 4 units ⟶ ◯   4 tens and 8 units ⟶ ◯

7 tens and 9 units ⟶ ◯   8 tens and 0 units ⟶ ◯

2 tens and 2 units ⟶ ◯   9 tens and 5 units ⟶ ◯

Draw the numbers on the tens and units chart.

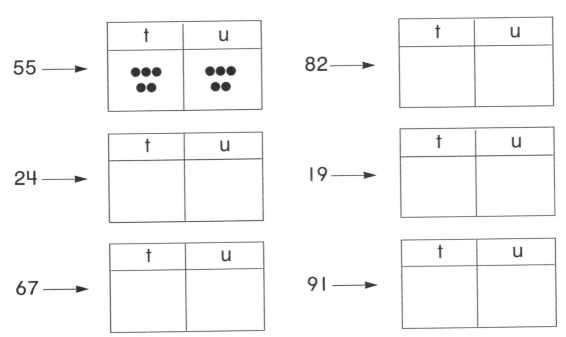

55 ⟶

t	u
●●● ●●	●●● ●●

82 ⟶

t	u

24 ⟶

t	u

19 ⟶

t	u

67 ⟶

t	u

91 ⟶

t	u

Draw the beads on the tens and unit strings, then add two more beads. Draw and write the new total.

t   u   t   u

2   **8**   **+**   **2**   **=**   **3**   **0**

t   u   t   u

3   **8**   **+**   **2**   **=**

t   u   t   u

5   **9**   **+**   **2**   **=**

Can you total the points for each child?

Which is the highest number of points above?

Read the words aloud, then write a sentence for your answer.

Jane won three points, then six points, then seven points.

What was the total number of Jane's points?

Can you do these sums? Remember to start at the units side?

Add	t. u.		t. u.		t. u.		t. u.
	2 6		2 6		2 6		2 6
	+ 4		+ 4		+ 4		+ 4
	———		———		———		———

	t. u.		t. u.		t. u.		t. u.
	1 9		1 1		7 7		8 4
	+ 2		+ 9		+ 3		+ 7
	———		———		———		———

Take away

	t. u.		t. u.		t. u.		t. u.
	2 6		3 2		6 6		4 5
	− 4		− 2		− 6		− 5
	———		———		———		———

	t. u.		t. u.		t. u.		t. u.
	5 3		2 9		4 3		9 8
	− 1		− 7		− 3		− 6
	———		———		———		———

Use the 100 square to check your answers to the sums above.

1	2	3	4	5	6	7	8	9	10
11	12	13	14	15	16	17	18	19	20
21	22	23	24	25	26	27	28	29	30
31	32	33	34	35	36	37	38	39	40
41	42	43	44	45	46	47	48	49	50
51	52	53	54	55	56	57	58	59	60
61	62	63	64	65	66	67	68	69	70
71	72	73	74	75	76	77	78	79	80
81	82	83	84	85	86	87	88	89	90
91	92	93	94	95	96	97	98	99	100

Add and take

10

$25+10=$ ☐

$36-10=$ ☐

$42+10=$ ☐

$55-10=$ ☐

$63+10=$ ☐

$77-10=$ ☐

$81+10=$ ☐

$99-10=$ ☐

Use the number lines to help you to add and subtract.

Add 3 →

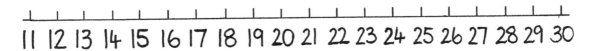

| | 12 13 14 15 16 17 18 19 20 21 22 23 24 25 26 27 28 29 30

11+3= ☐   11+3= ☐   11+3= ☐   11+3= ☐

← Take 3

19 20 21 22 23 24 25 26 27 28 29 30 31 32 33

24−3= ☐   26−3= ☐   22−3= ☐   31−3= ☐

Add 4 →

36 37 38 39 40 41 42 43 44 45 46 47 48 49 50 51 52 53 54

37+4= ☐   39+4= ☐   40+4= ☐   46+4= ☐

← Take 4

50 51 52 53 54 55 56 57 58 59 60 61 62 63 64 65 66 67 68 69

69−4= ☐   63−4= ☐   61−4= ☐   68−4= ☐

Increase each price by 20p. Cross out the old price and write the
Write the new one

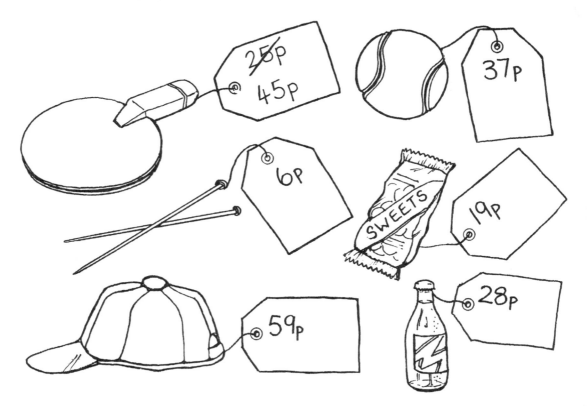

Can you do these sums?

9+3=	10−7=	5+6=
19+3=	20−7=	15+6=
29+3=	30−7=	25+6=
39+3=	40−7=	35+6=
49+3=	50−7=	45+6=

Read the questions aloud before you work out the answers.
Remember to write a word as well as a number in your answers.

The toy aeroplane costs 90p.
The toy boat costs 40p.
What is the difference in
price between the two?

<table><tr><td>

</td></tr></table>

Peter was 7 years old.
His brother was 4 years older
than this. How old was Peter's
brother?

Mary collected 17 conkers.
Kate collected 24 conkers.
How many conkers did the
girls have between them?

Colour half of each shape. The sign for half is ½. Write this sign on the two halves of each shape.

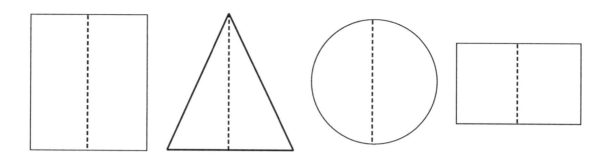

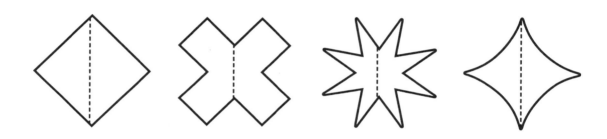

Write half of each number.

12 _halved is_ → [6]

6 ⟶ [ ]

2 ⟶ [ ]

8 ⟶ [ ]

10 ⟶ [ ]

Double each number.

6 _doubled is_ → [12]

7 ⟶ [ ]

9 ⟶ [ ]

3 ⟶ [ ]

8 ⟶ [ ]

Read the number stories aloud before you work out the answer.

At the party Mashood filled a litre jug with lemonade. He poured half of the lemonade into some paper cups. How much lemonade was left in the jug?

_____

Anne cut 2 metres of rope in half to make 2 skipping ropes. What length was each skipping rope?

_____

Sara's piano lesson lasted for 30 minutes. David's lesson lasted half as long. For how many minutes did David's lesson last?

_____

Read these sums aloud, then complete the four sums in the other boxes.

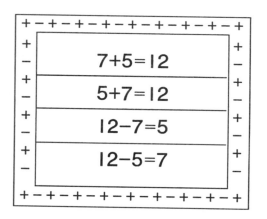

7+5=12

5+7=12

12−7=5

12−5=7

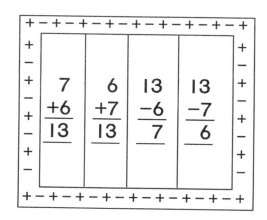

7	6	13	13
+6	+7	−6	−7
13	13	7	6

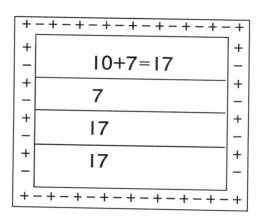

10+7=17

7

17

17

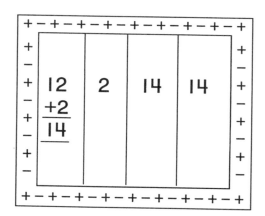

12	2	14	14
+2			
14			

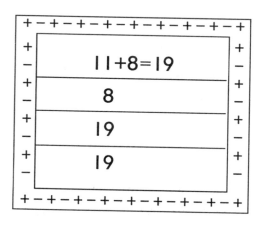

11+8=19

8

19

19

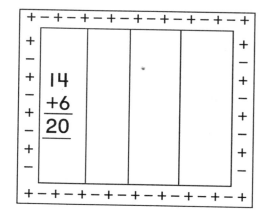

14			
+6			
20			

32